Printed and published
in Great Britain by
D.C. Thomson & Co., Ltd.,
185 Fleet Street, London.
© D.C. THOMSON & CO., LTD.,
1995.

(Certain stories do not appear
exactly as originally published.)

ISBN 0-85116-594X

DANDY AND BEANO

AND

101 GREAT STORIES

JIMMY AND HIS MAGIC PATCH

1 — It was Saturday afternoon and Jimmy Watson, with his home-made pirate outfit, walked down to the pond near the village. It was as he reached it that he noticed two of his pals striding towards him. "Hi, chums!" he yelled, waving his wooden sword. "Let's get aboard our raft and play pirates again." One of the lads waved a derisive hand. "Bah!" he said. "We're going to the pictures to see a real pirate picture!"

2 — Jimmy's face fell as they walked away and left him at the edge of the pond. "If only I had enough money to go to the pictures," he muttered. "I wish I could see real pirates, too." Swoosh! His magic patch on the seat of his pants took the hint and Jimmy found himself whizzing through space. With a bump he landed — on the deck of an old-time sailing ship! His eyes opened wide as he saw what was happening on board.

3 — A band of ruffians had mutinied on the ship and over-powered the captain and his trusty men. The mutineers had run up the pirate flag and the leader was now ordering one of his men to lash the captain, helplessly tied to a dangling rope. It was then that the evil bosun noticed Jimmy. "Ho!" he roared. "Who's this come to interfere?" Unconsciously Jimmy raised his wooden sword as the bearded ruffian approached.

4 — A bellow of laughter came from the bosun. "So it's sword-play you want?" he roared. "On guard then, dog!" Jimmy clumsily warded off an evil thrust with his wooden sword, but he knew how helpless he was. The cutlass flickered in and out far too quickly for Jimmy to see and suddenly his sword jerked in his hand. An evil grin flooded the bosun's weather-beaten face. He had cut Jimmy's wooden sword in two!

5 — Jimmy groaned and dropped the useless handle. The bosun stepped towards him. Like lightning the lad turned and raced away down the deck. A wild yell of fury came from the bosun as he started in pursuit. "Wait till I catch you!" he roared. "I'll dangle you from the highest yard-arm!" Jimmy leaped for the shrouds at the side of the ship. The lad had never moved faster than he did then.

6 — He was halfway up before the pirate had started to climb. But the evil bosun was no new hand at this game like Jimmy. He soon shortened the space between them. Scrambling upwards, well beyond the crow's nest, Jimmy glanced down. Cutlass between teeth, the bosun was barely a yard behind him. Jimmy's pulses were racing as he started to climb still further up the mast. Soon the bosun would be able to cut him down.

7 — He kept climbing until at last he was stuck. Clinging to the mast with one hand, he desperately snatched his fountain pen from his pocket. The bosun gave an evil laugh as he raised his cutlass just as Jimmy jerked at the lever of the pen with his thumb. It had been newly filled and a thick stream of ink shot out — into the bosun's eye! The shock made him release his hold on the mast.

8 — With a startled cry he dropped downwards. His cutlass fell with him. The men's faces on deck changed from grins to dismay as their leader dropped, howling, from the mast-top. They were too excited watching him to notice that the falling cutlass sheered through the rope holding the captain of the ship. In no time he managed to free himself now that his arms were loose enough to move his hands freely.

9 — Stealthily he stepped behind one of the mutineers and swung an arm about the man's neck. The man's cry for help turned into a low gasp as the captain's arm tightened on his windpipe. The mutineer was helpless to prevent the captain helping himself to his cutlass and pistol. Jimmy was the only person aboard who noticed this quiet struggle as he slid quickly to the deck. The mutineers were watching their leader struggling in the water.

10 — It was only when the captain shouted his order to lay down their arms that they awoke to the situation. By then it was too late. A steady hand covered them with a pistol which none of the yellow-livered mutineers dared to move against. Under the captain's orders Jimmy opened the deck house and freed his trusty men. A few of the mutineers threw a rope to the evil bosun and he was helped aboard.

11 — Dripping wet, he faced the captain. He realised he was trapped, but a gleam of hope shone in his eyes as the captain spoke. "There's only one way to deal with traitors," he roared, and flung a rapier at the bosun's feet. "Here, take this." "A fight to the finish," the bosun thought. There was still a chance. He grabbed the rapier and thrust at the captain. The onlookers were silent as the steel clashed.

12 — The swords were like flickering shafts of light. Once, twice, the captain drew blood, until the bosun could fight no longer. He threw down his sword and cried for mercy. With his disgruntled men he was tied up and locked away. "You made that possible," the captain said, turning to Jimmy. "Thanks for —" but that was as far as he got. Jimmy suddenly found himself back in modern times, thinking of his latest exciting adventure.

DENNIS THE MASCOT

As the story on the opposite page shows, Dennis's dad may be the oldest winger in town, but Dennis himself has 'scrum' out of it rather well. He's been chosen as official mascot for the Little League — an organised rugby league for youngsters aged 7 to 11, sponsored by the 36 Professional Rugby League sides. Dennis will be 'booting' an appearance on lots of Little League merchandise, and our photograph shows Dennis along with some of the Little Leaguers who played an exhibition game before the Great Britain versus Australia 1st Test at Wembley last year.

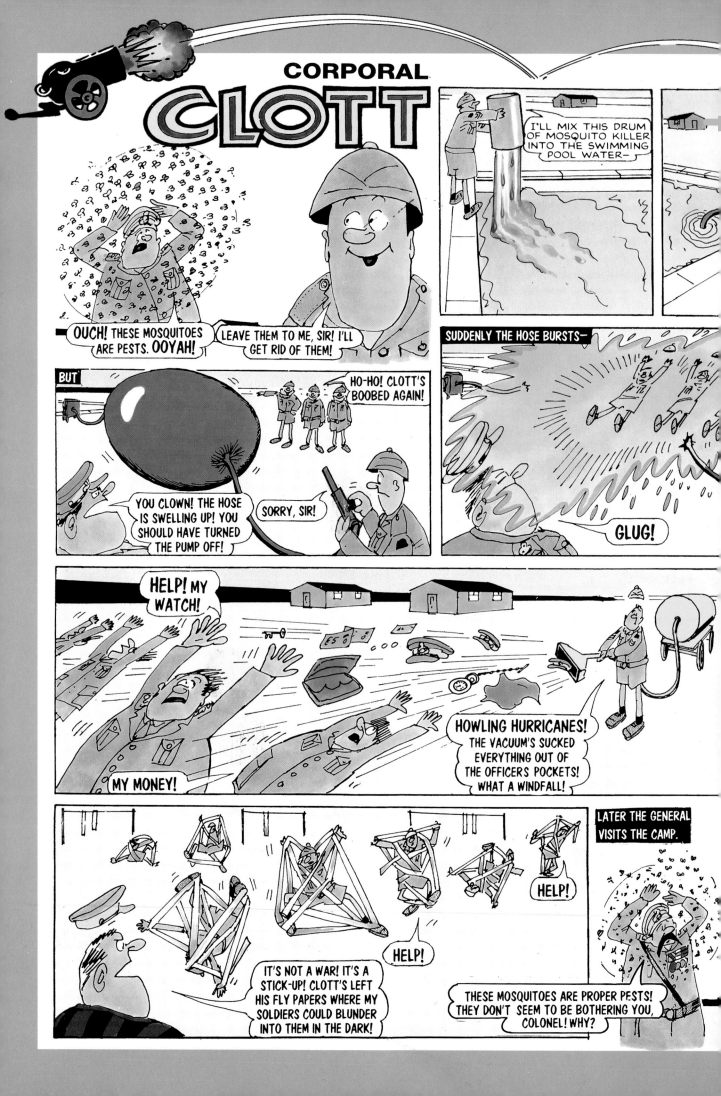

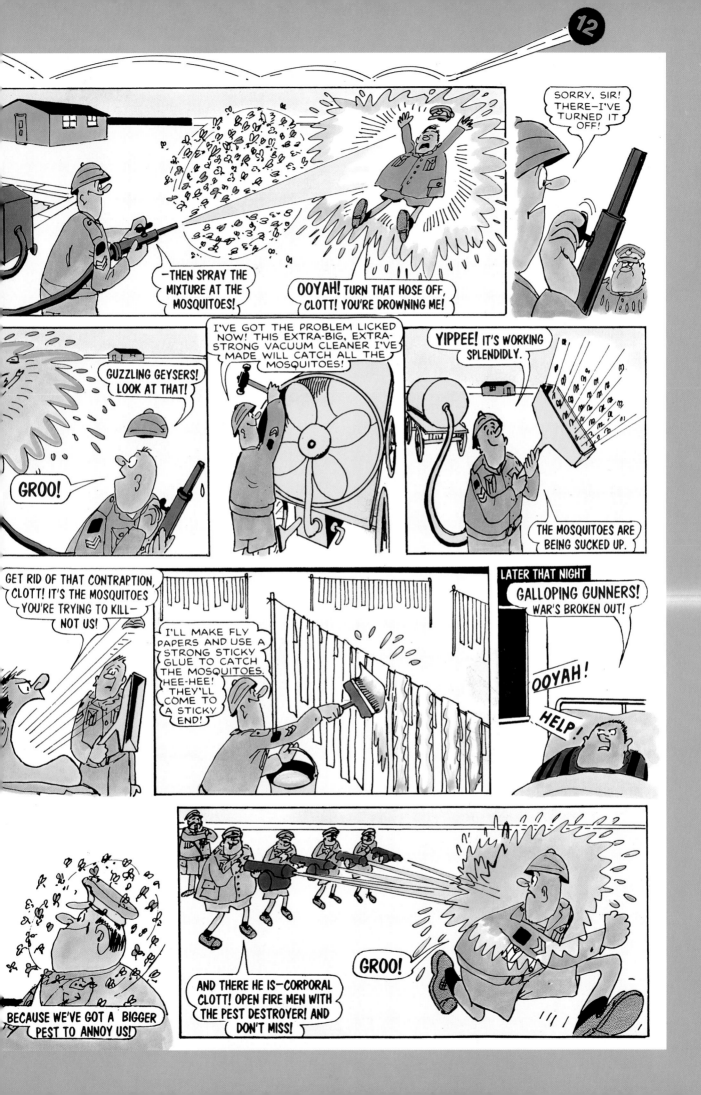

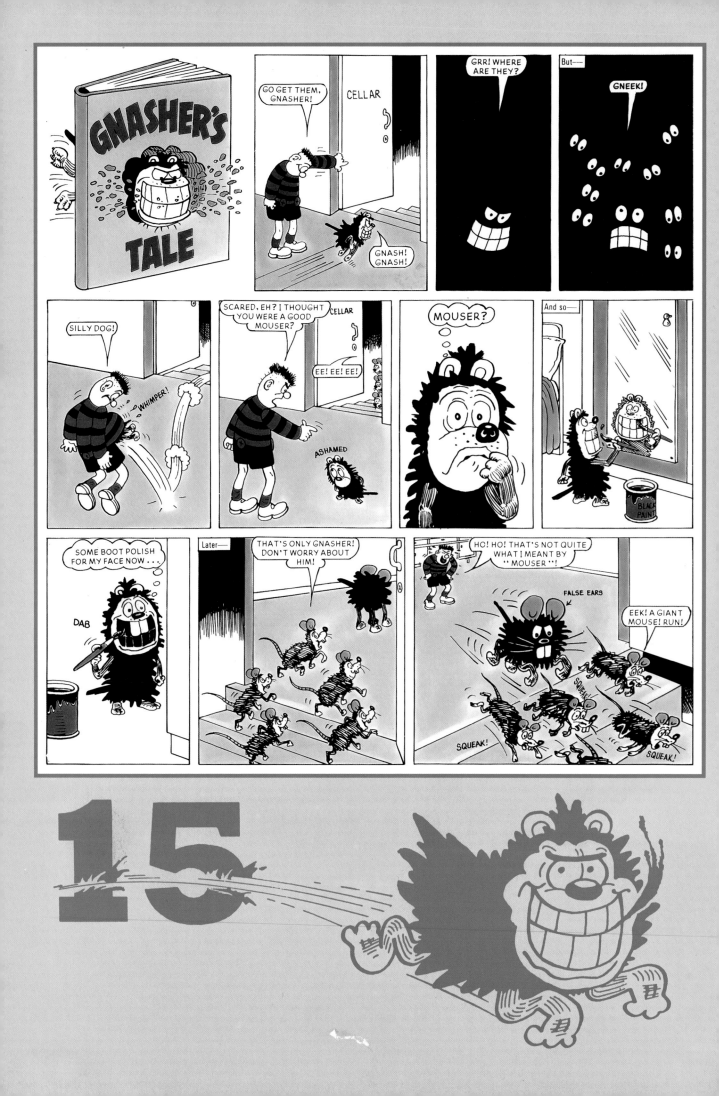

SOCK IT TO 'EM!

Dennis is a menace from the top of his head to the tips of his toes — ESPECIALLY his toes, according to a recent report in a daily newspaper. When a Scottish lawyer was given a pair of Dennis The Menace musical socks by his wife, he never dreamt that the socks would start playing Jingle Bells in court, during a trial. The poor lawyer ended up with a face redder than the stripes on Dennis' jersey as he unsuccessfully tried to silence the socks, before admitting de-FEET!

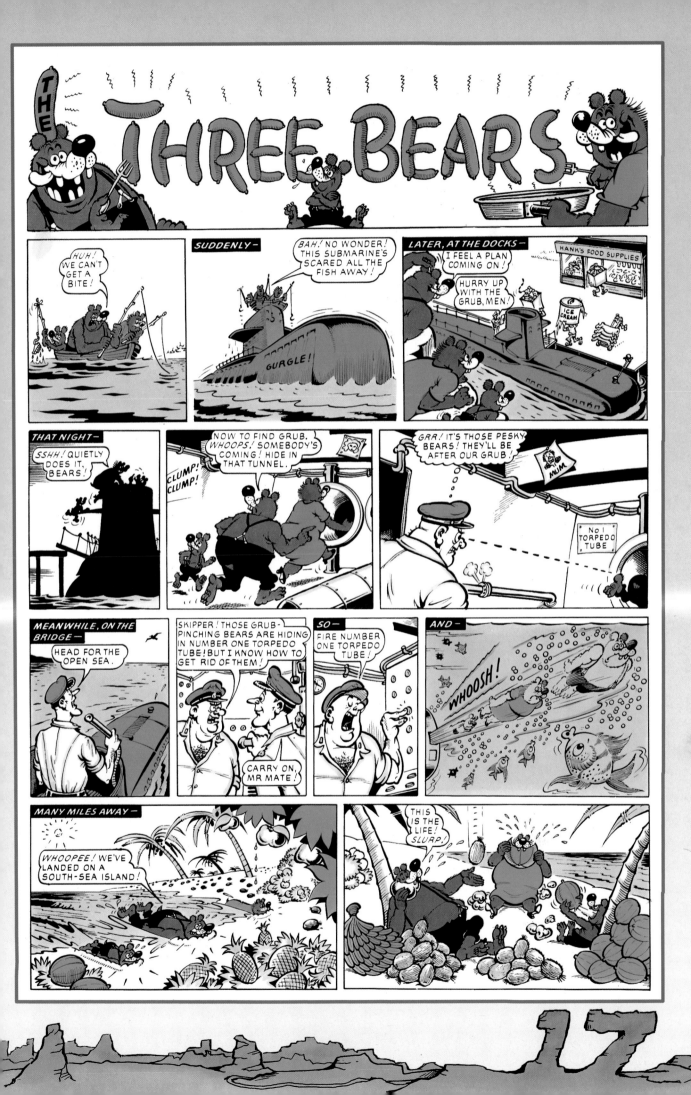

101 GREAT

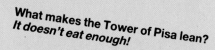

Two mind-readers met. One said to the other, "You're feeling fine. How am I?"

Right, class! How do we know heat makes things expand?
Summer days are longer than Winter ones, Sir.

Which day of the week is Gnasher's favourite?
Chewsday.

How far can a pirate ship go?
Fifteen miles to the "galleon"!

Ouch! A crab just bit my toe.
Which one?
I don't know — all crabs look alike to me.

How do you keep a silly-billy in suspense?
I don't know.
I'll tell you tomorrow.

Why are elephants large, lumpy-shaped and grey?
Because if they were small, round and white they'd be peppermints.

Is there any soup on the menu?
There was, but I wiped it off!

Where does Tarzan buy his clothes?
At a jungle sale.

What happened to the man who sat up all night wondering where the sun had gone?
It suddenly dawned on him.

You look worried, Smiffy. What's wrong?
I can't understand why my sister has two brothers and I've only got one!

What is the difference between a TV and a newspaper?
I don't know.
Have you ever tried to swat a fly with a TV?

Why did the sailor grab a bar of soap when his ship sank?
So he could wash himself ashore.

What should I buy my uncle for his hundredth birthday?
A cake with a hundred candles and a fire extinguisher.

It must be difficult for a man with a moustache to eat soup.
Yes — it's quite a strain.

What makes the Tower of Pisa lean?
It doesn't eat enough!

I'll teach you to throw things at my greenhouse!
I wish you would — I've had ten shots and haven't hit it yet!

What do you give an undernourished gnome?
Elf-raising flour.

What smells nice and rides a horse in the Wild West?
The Cologne Ranger!

Did you feel better after you'd been to the dentist's?
Yes — he wasn't in!

You've got your shoes on the wrong feet.
But these are the only feet I have!

My pet snake plays chess with me.
That's amazing! It must be a really intelligent snake.
Not really — I beat him every time!

Your hair needs cutting badly, sir.
Well, I don't know anyone who can cut it as badly as you!

Why were you kept in after school today?
I didn't know where the Orkneys were, Dad.
Well, in future, just remember where you put things!

HA-HA-HA-HA! HEE-HEE! HO-HO-HO! HA-HA

GAGS

PART 1

My dog doesn't have a tail. How do you know when he's happy?
He stops biting me!

I'm going to save my pocket money and buy a farm ten miles long and one centimetre wide. What are you going to grow on it?
Spaghetti!

Doctor, every time I eat a sweet I feel like giving large sums of money away.
Sit down. Care for a jellybaby?

What do sea monsters have for their lunch?
Fish and ships.

What happened when the frog broke down on the motorway?
I've no idea.
It got "toad" away!

Where do American cows live?
Moo York.

Why is it difficult to keep a secret in cold weather?
Because your teeth chatter.

Why are you all wet?
My coat fell into the duck pond.
Then why is the rest of you wet?
I was inside the coat.

HO-HO-HO-HO!

Why does a bald-headed man have no use for keys?
Because he has no locks!

What exams do farmers have to take?
Hay-levels.

How does a sparrow with engine trouble manage to land safely?
With a sparrowchute!

What did you get the small medal for?
For singing.
What did you get the big medal for?
For stopping.

Will my measles be better next week, Doctor?
Well, I hate to make rash promises!

What is the fastest part on a car?
The dash-board!

What do you call a baby whale?
I don't know.
A little squirt!

I want you to give me the names of five animals found in Africa?
Four lions and a giraffe, sir!

Why do bees hum?
Because they don't know the words!

What's black and hairy and is surrounded by water?
A North Sea oil WIG!

What's a ghost's favourite game?
Haunt The Thimble.

Doctor, my family thinks I'm crazy.
Why?
Because I like sausages.
Nonsense! I like sausages, too!
You do? You must come round and see my collection. I have hundreds of them.

I was teacher's pet today at school.
Eh? You were?
Yes, she put me in a cage at the back of the class!

You're sure this plant will bloom every hundred years?
Well if it doesn't, just bring it back.

HA!

HEE-HEE-HEE!

I bet I can make a funnier face than you.
No wonder! Look at the start you've got!

Where do spiders play football?
Webley!

Doctor! Doctor! I swallowed a clock last week.
Goodness! Why didn't you come to me sooner?
I didn't want to alarm anyone.

When you come to my party tomorrow, just ring the doorbell with your elbow.
Why with my elbow?
Well, you're not coming empty-handed, are you?

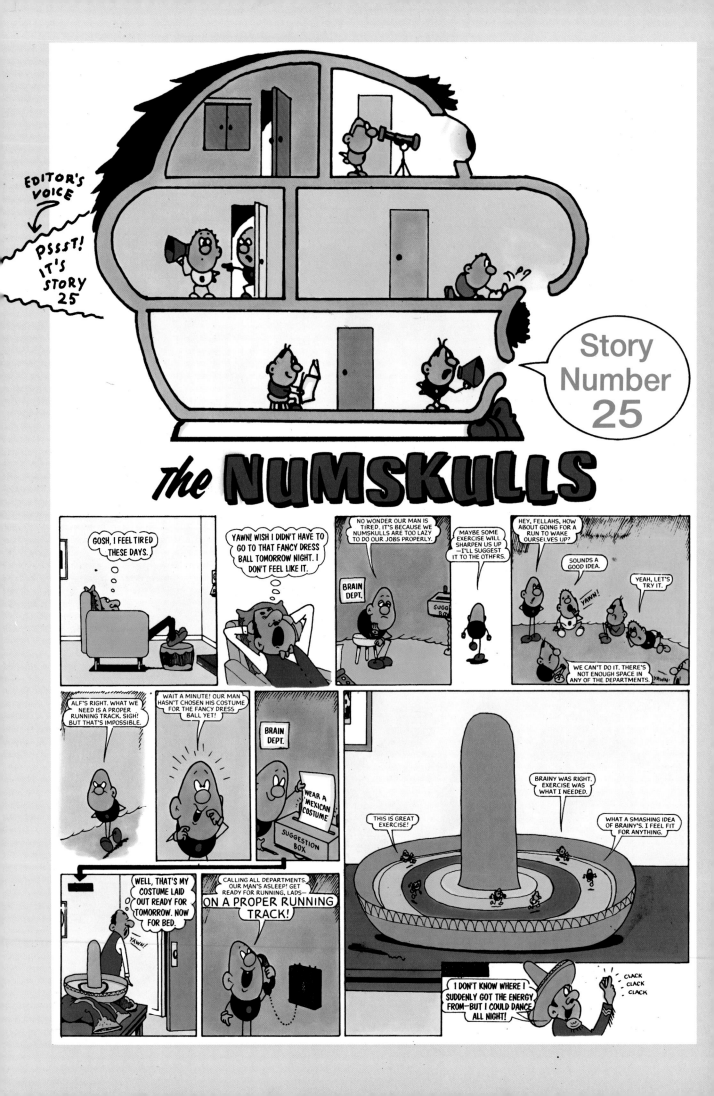

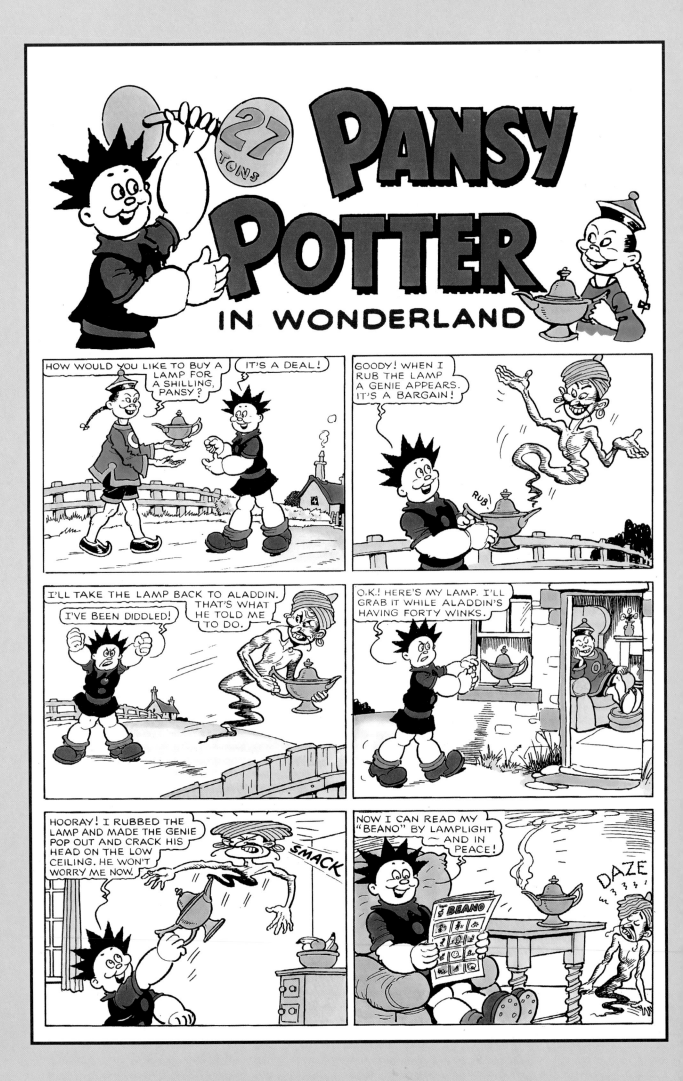

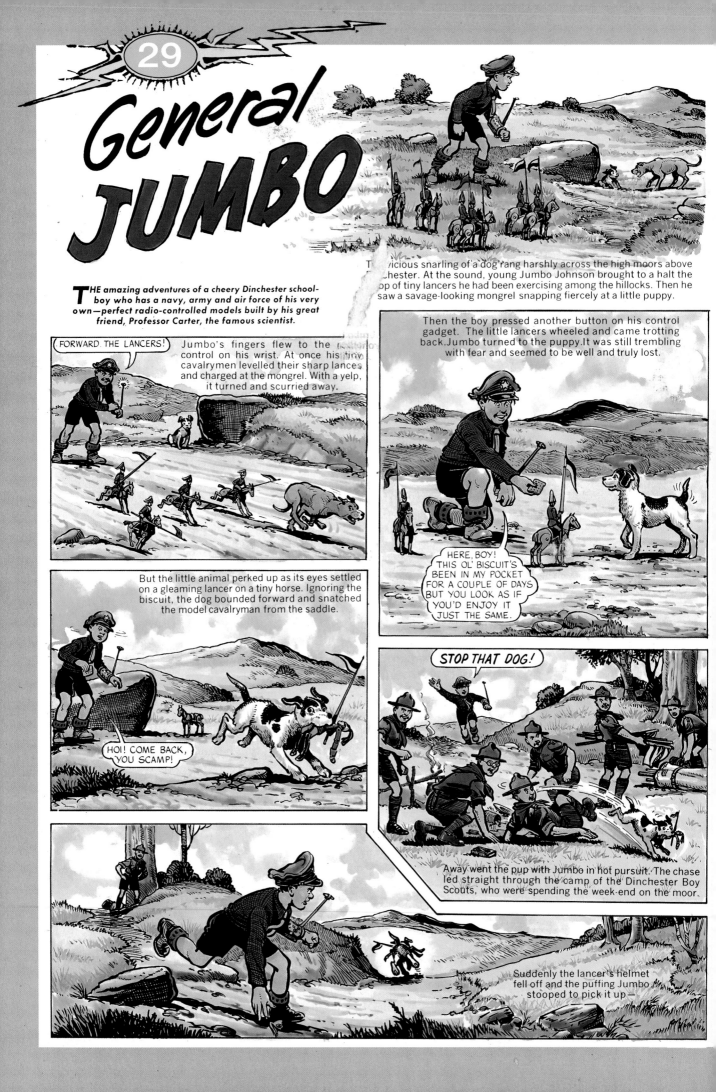

—When he looked up again the pup had disappeared! Then, from some bushes, the lad heard a muffled yelp. He raced towards the sound and, next second, he was dropping like a stone.

Jumbo hit the hard ground with a thump that knocked all the breath from him. As he rose groggily to his feet he saw the pup beside him. The lad dizzily looked around. Both he and the dog were in a deep, narrow pit with sheer sides. There was no hope of climbing out. He began to shout for help. Perhaps the Boy Scouts would hear him . . . But the sound of his voice was muffled by the sides of the deep pit.

Jumbo examined the whimpering pup more carefully. Its left foreleg appeared to be broken. He had to get help — but how? . . . Then a plan flashed into his mind. He pulled from his pocket a pencil, tied his handkerchief to it, and put the pencil in the lancer's free hand. Then he tossed the model out of the pit.

Deftly Jumbo worked his radio control. The pocket lancer stood upright and began to signal over and over again in semaphore the letters SOS . . . SOS . . . It was half an hour before the Scouts spotted the signaller.

LOOK, BOYS! SOMEBODY'S IN TROUBLE!

True to their motto, the Scouts were prepared for the emergency. Ron Adams, the patrol leader, unwound a light, strong rope from his waist and, Jumbo, clutching the pup, was pulled up to safety.

WELL DONE, JUMBO! YOU AND YOUR MODELS HAVE CERTAINLY DONE YOUR GOOD DEED FOR THE DAY!

While Jumbo rounded up the rest of his lancers, the Scouts got busy fitting splints on the pup's injured leg. Then they put the little dog in one of their carts. In a few moments Jumbo had four lancers harnessed to the cart. And, at a fast frot, he took them towards the vet's house in Dinchester. Soon the injured pup would be returned, safe and well, to its owner, thanks to the smallest cavalrymen in the world!

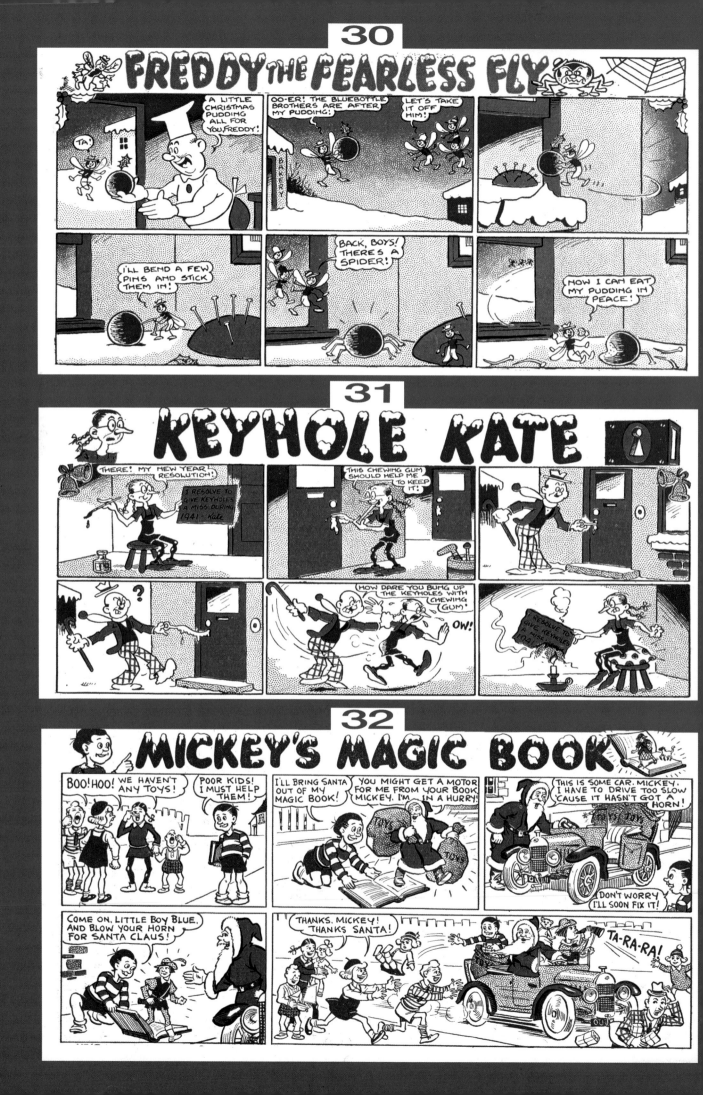

33

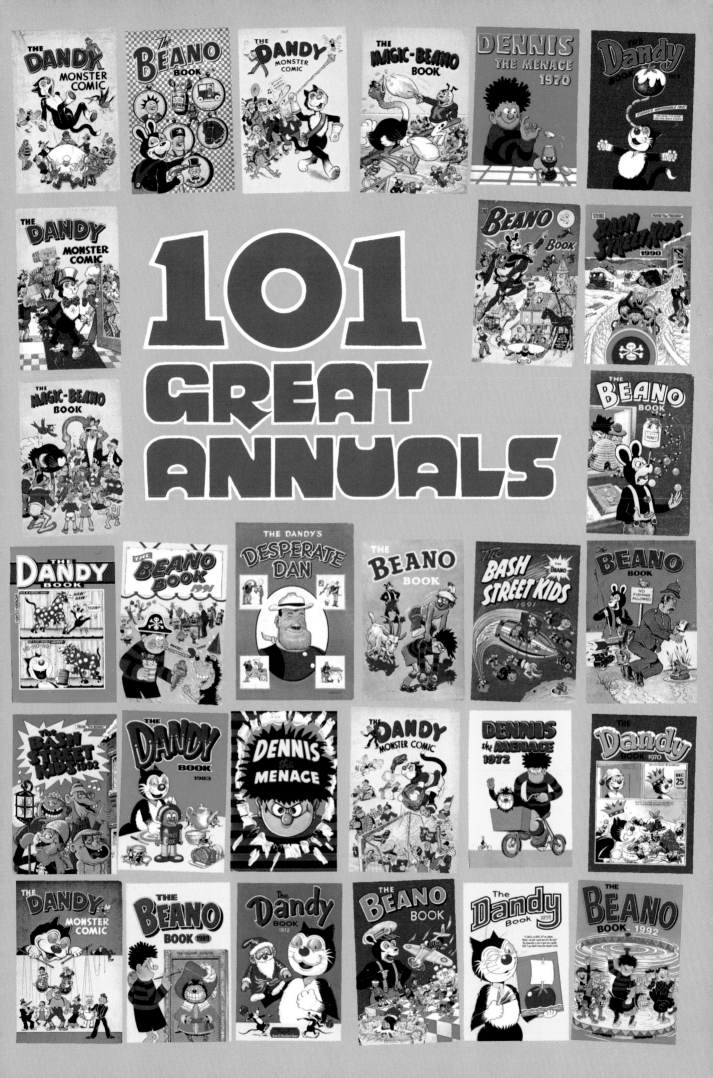

101 GREAT ANNUALS

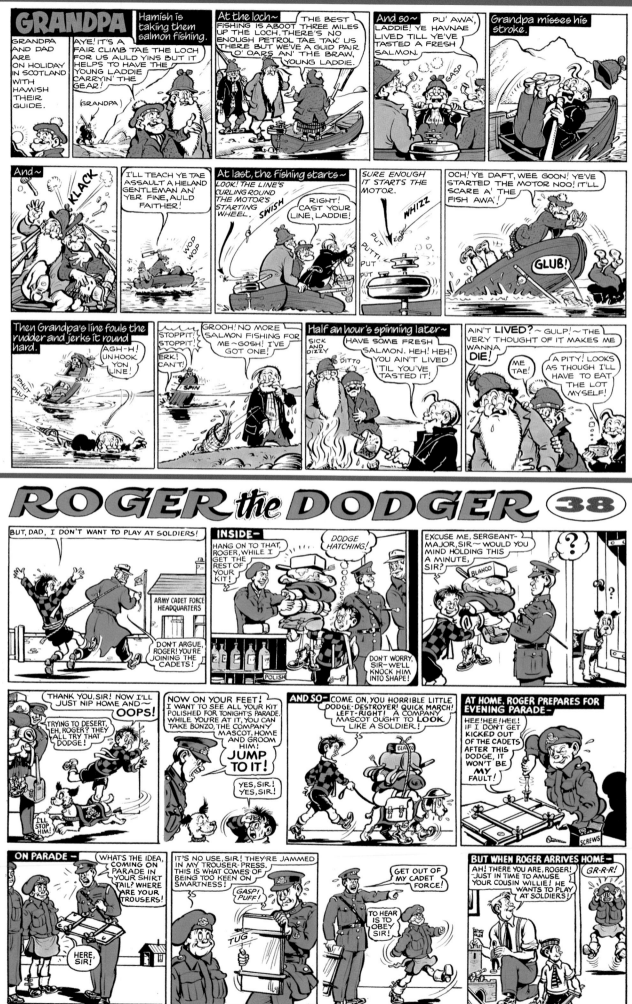

the Bash Street Kids

DESPERATE DAN

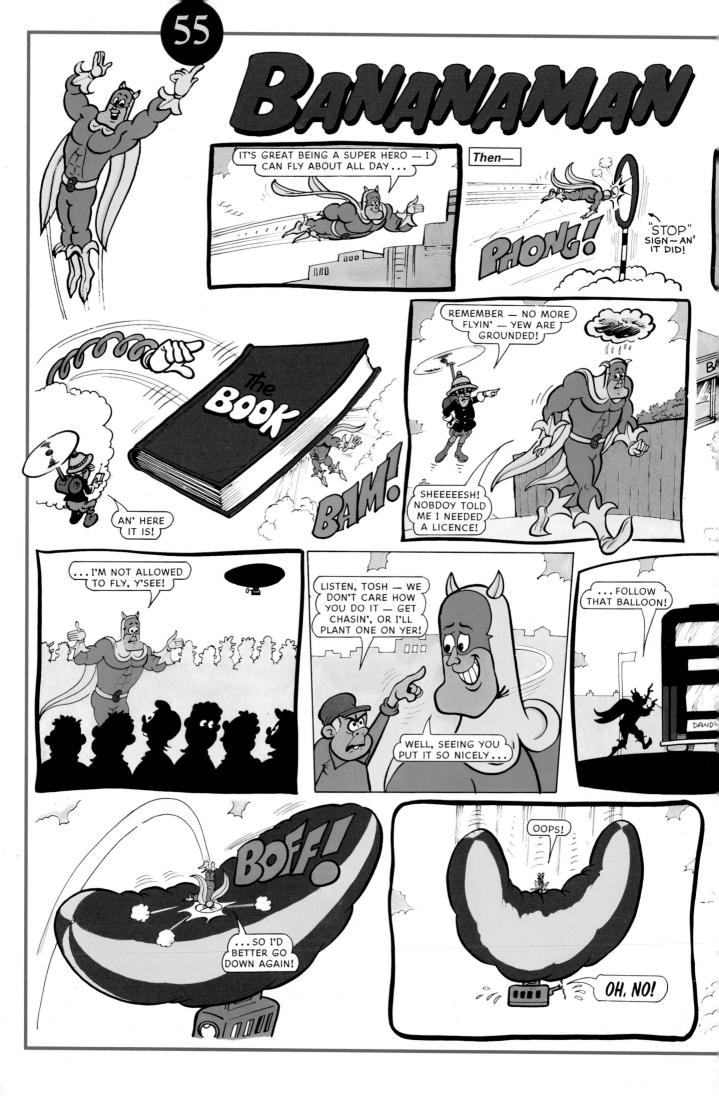

READ ALL ABOUT 'EM!

TELL MUM AND DAD ABOUT THIS

THE HOLY TERROR FROM "THE BEANO"

DENNIS the MENACE

A NEW ADVENTURE EVERY WEEK IN THE **WEEKLY NEWS** 2½d

ON SALE THURSDAY

It's not unknown for comic superstars to make the headlines. When Dennis The Menace celebrated his 50th birthday in 1988 hundreds of newspapers reported the great event. But there was a time when legends of the British comic scene appeared in a top-selling newspaper EVERY week. For over 20 years, from 1946, Black Bob, The Dandy Wonderdog featured in a nine-picture strip in THE WEEKLY NEWS and in 1953 Dennis The Menace was given a strip of his own in the same newspaper.

BLACK BOB'S BIG ADVENTURE!

YES, THE DANDY WONDER DOG IS IN THE THICK OF A GREAT ADVENTURE JUST NOW. WHY NOT SHARE THE THRILLS WITH HIM? ALL YOU HAVE TO DO IS GET A COPY OF The **WEEKLY NEWS** THE PAPER WITH THE FAMOUS BLACK BOB PICTURE—STORY EVERY WEEK.

F

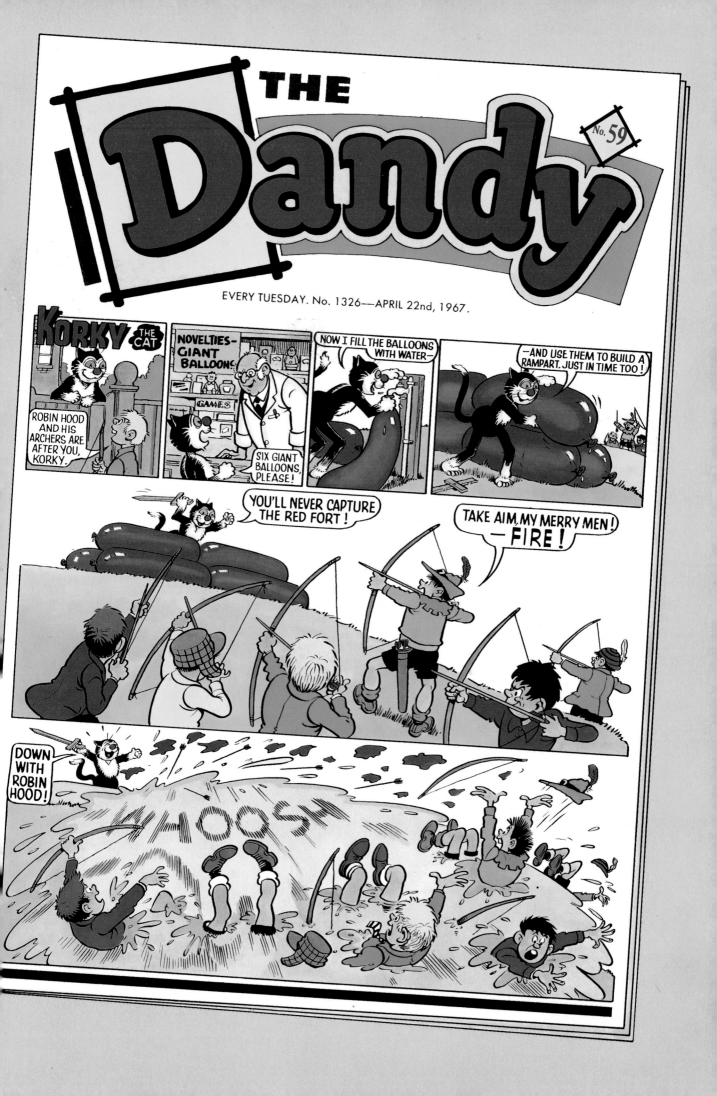

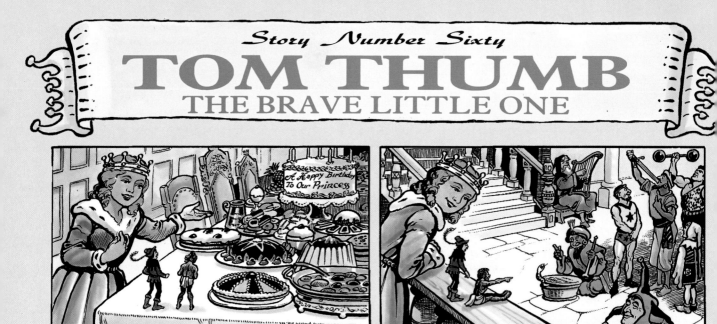

1 —In delight our chums are gazing
　　At that tasty birthday-spread,
　　They're invited, and the Princess
　　Means to see her guests well fed!

2 —Next they watch the entertainers,
　　Folk of every kind and size.
　　Soon there's going to be a contest,
　　Where the King will give a prize!

3 —Now they've come upon a bully,
　　What he's done is plain to see,
　　Knowing those frogs were much more clever,
　　He had set his cruel pet free!

4 —Since the frogs are dead he's certain
　　That his rat will win the day,
　　But our chums are quickly scheming
　　Not to let him have his way!

5 —Tom's idea is quite a winner,
　　Here they'll get a change of "togs"!
　　That unhappy lad is laughing.
　　They'll be fine performing frogs!

6 —Just in time they reach the Palace,
　　Their performance goes on next,
　　"Here's our chance to teach that bully,"
　　Whispers Tom, "Won't he be vexed!"

7 —Up they're put on to the table,
   Where they make a Royal bow,
   King and Princess gaze in wonder,
   What will they be up to now?

8 —Tom and Tinkel take the biscuit,
   Frogs playing leap-frog seem so queer,
   While the King and courtiers chuckle
   That big bully gives a leer!

9 —"I'll teach them!" the bad lad mutters,
   Setting free his fiercesome rat,
   Tom and Tinkel flee, determined
   That he won't get off with that!

10 —With the fork they've turned the tables,
    Terrified, the rat turns tail,
    As for that big, boastful bully,
    He's being turned into the jail!

11 —Now to round off their performance,
    Those cute frogs begin to spell,
    Frogs can't spell? Well just watch closely,
    So far they're doing pretty well!

12 —That poor youngster's really smiling,
    While the chums could dance with glee,
    Now their friend is well rewarded,
    Their reward is — birthday tea!

WILLIE'S WHIZZER BROOM

PLIP! *Plop-plop!* "Drat that leaking roof!" growled Grandad Meldrum as drips of water plopped on his bald head. His grandson, young Willie Meldrum, was annoyed with the leaks, too. He didn't like rain dripping into his soup. But the slater was too busy to come and repair the roof.

2 — At last Willie could stand it no longer. He sat astride his Whizzer Broom and pressed the secret switch. *Whoosh!* At once the amazing broom whisked him through time to the year 2500. "Surely someone there will have some fancy gadgets for repairing roofs," Willie murmured to himself.

3 — That's what he thought! Rain was pouring down when he landed. The broom dropped him in front of an open door through which water was streaming. Inside Willie could see a man vainly trying to repair a leaking ceiling. "Can I give you a hand?" Willie called. "We might stop the leak between us."

4 — "Thanks," replied the man. "But we can't till those stupid weather controllers switch the rain off. Look at the calendar." Willie looked, and wondered. "Day number 233 — RAIN," it said. Tuk, as the man was called, explained that the weather was decided in advance, and controlled by scientists.

5 — "Why don't you ask them to stop the rain?" Willie asked Tuk. "There's no harm in trying," Tuk agreed and, protected from the rain by his special nylon umbrella-robe, they set off for the Weather Control Station. "We've got to get past this guard before I can see the controllers," Tuk growled.

6 — But when Tuk asked to be allowed into the station, the guard refused. "No admittance to anyone," he growled. Tuk argued with him, but the guard refused to alter his decision. And while the two men argued, Willie began to fiddle with a strange gadget which was sitting on the ground beside the guard.

7 — "I wonder what this plunger is for?" Willie muttered, giving it a prod. Immediately there came a sharp hissing noise from the gadget and a blast of air shot out of the hose which was attached to it. The air got under the nylon umbrella, which Willie had been holding while Tuk did the arguing. "Wow! I'm flying!" gasped Willie as the blast swept him up in the air, over the wall, and into the Control Station. The guard stood and gaped. That gadget was a blaster for getting rid of argumentative callers — and here it was being used to get someone past him!

8 — Willie landed with a thud in the courtyard of the Control Station and in a flash he realised that, since Tuk couldn't get in to have the rain stopped, Willie himself might have a chance to do the job. Before the guard arrived, Willie was hiding in a small building.

9 — Willie kept out of sight in the building until he heard the guard stamp off, then he went looking for the man who controlled the weather. Willie didn't find the Controller, but he found a set of odd-looking machines marked, "Hail, Wind, Snow, Rain." Sparks were shooting from the rain machine. "I'll stop the rain," Willie chuckled, whipping out his catapult. He wasn't going to risk touching those things! *Ping!* He fired.

10 — But the pebble bounced off the rain machine and struck the control button on the hail machine. In a surprisingly short time the weather changed. Hailstones as big as ping-pong balls hurtled down from the black clouds which had been hanging over the town. The people in the street scurried around, looking for shelter. There were no shop doorways in the streets of the future, however, and howls of pain and anger filled the air.

11 — "Ouch! I've had enough of this!" roared one burly fellow. "I'm going to the Weather Control Station to complain." Half a dozen others at once decided to go with him and they all charged towards the entrance. More and more people joined the group and by the time they reached the gates there was a huge mob of people behind the leader. "We've had enough of your Weather Control! Turn off these machines," they roared as they swept across the courtyard.

12 — The controllers themselves were pretty fed up of the weather. The hailstones were so big that their glass roof had been shattered, and they were yelling in pain as the icy stones hit them. "Who's the head one among you?" demanded the leader of the mob. The shaking controller owned up. "Make him give us some decent weather," Willie was told. So, with Willie's catapult aimed at him, the controller stopped the hail and used the wind machine to blow the clouds away.

13 — Presently the sun began to shine. "Hooray!" cried Tuk. "Good weather — and it's all thanks to you, Willie. What can I do to repay you?" Willie told how he had come looking for a means of repairing his roof and Tuk at once took a collection from all the grateful townspeople. He got quite a lot of money.

14 — With the money he bought a wonderful roof-repairing machine and, back in 1956, Willie found it was as easy to use as Grandma's vacuum cleaner. He supported himself on a rope stretched between the chimneys and pushed the strange machine back and forward over the troublesome hole in the slates.

15 — With a harsh grating noise the machine went to work. In no time at all there was a gleaming patch over the leaky slates. "Well, Willie," said Grandad, "that machine's done a great job. I think, when the rain goes off, we'll do the rest of the roof, too. And then we'll never have another leak."

101 GREAT

Which clothing keeps you warmest?
A blazer!

Can you stand on your head?
No — it's too high.

Have you heard about the man who woke up with his bedroom full of aeroplanes?
No.
He'd left the "landing" light on!

Where do farmers leave their pigs when they go to town?
At porking meters!

Who'd win a fight between a dog and a hedgehog?
The hedgehog would win on points!

Why did the crook saw off the legs of his bed after the bank robbery?
Because he had to lie low for a while.

What did Smiffy (the daft Bash St. Kid) call his pet zebra?
Spot!

What do ghosts have for dessert?
I-SCREAM!

The man who invented door knockers was given the first NO-BELL (Nobel) prize.

When do you put a frog in someone's wellington boots?
When you can't find a mouse.

Have you any invisible ink, Shopkeeper?
Certainly — what colour?

Why do cows wear cow bells?
Because their horns don't work.

How can you stop your nose from running?
Stick your foot out and trip it up.

How do you make anti-freeze?
Pinch all her blankets!

Why does a golfer take two pairs of trousers with him?
In case he gets a hole in one!

What does the Abominable Snowman like for dinner?
Spag-yeti!

What do hedgehogs love to eat?
Prickled onions!

Hey, who gave you that black eye?
No-one! I had to fight for it!

I had a dream last night that I was eating a giant marshmallow. When I woke up my pillow had gone!

What's the best thing for putting in pies?
Teeth!

What did one wall say to the other wall?
Meet you at the corner!

What kind of sound irritates an oyster?
A noisy noise annoys an oyster.

What do you cut the waves with?
A sea-saw!

What time is it when an elephant sits on the fence?
I don't know — what time is it when an elephant sits on the fence?
Time to get a new fence!

What would you do if this plane broke down in mid-air?
Get out and push, of course!

HA-HA-HA-HA!

HEE HEE

O-HO!

GAGS
PART 2

How do you get an elephant up a tree?
Sit him on an acorn and wait twenty years.

How do you get an elephant down from a tree?
Sit him on a leaf and wait till the autumn!

HA-HA!

Waiter, why have you got your fingers in my soup?
Because it's very cold in the kitchen!

What has five fingers and drives a tractor?
A farm hand.

If red houses are made of red bricks and blue houses are made of blue bricks what are green houses made of?
Glass.

What did the policeman say to his chest?
You're under a vest.

Did you get my slippers soled?
Yes — I got 50p for them!

HEE!

How do you join the Police?
Handcuff them all together.

Which is the smartest-looking vegetable?
A potato in its jacket!

Will you have beans on toast?
I suppose I'll have to, if you have no plates!

Why are fishmongers never generous?
Because their business makes them sell fish.

How did Smiffy hurt himself whilst raking up leaves?
He fell out of the tree!

Hey, I just saved 50p by running home behind a bus!
Huh! You could have saved £3 by running home behind a taxi!

What trees should deck chairs be made from?
Beech trees!

HO-HO-HO-HO!

Why does a glow worm glow?
Because he only eats light meals.

What did the scarf say to the hat?
You go on ahead and I'll just hang around.

Why do firemen wear red braces?
To hold up their trousers.

Why are tall people the laziest?
Because they lie longest in bed.

There's a hole in the bottom of the boat!
Don't worry — I'll make another hole to let the water out!

Doctor, Doctor, I feel like a bridge!
What's come over you?
Three lorries, four motorbikes and a Rolls Royce!

If a buttercup is yellow, what colour is a hiccup?
Burple!

What was the first message sent by smoke signal?
Help! My blanket's on fire!

When is a bucket unwell?
When it is a little pail (pale).

Why did Smiffy put a clock under his pillow?
He wanted to wake up on time!

I saw 24 men standing under an umbrella, and none of them got wet. Must have been a big umbrella.
No, it wasn't raining!

Why did the Boy Scout feel dizzy?
Because he did so many good turns!

HEE-HEE-HEE!

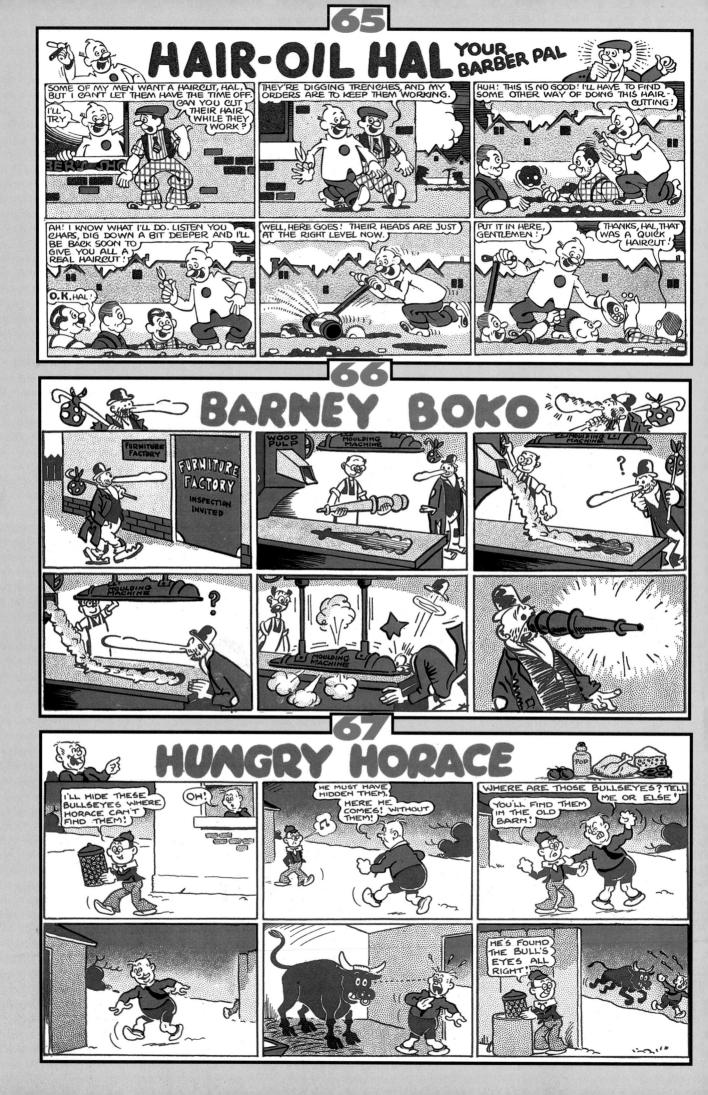

CHARLIE THE CHIMP

*S*NORT! *Snort! Grunt! Grunt!* It was feeding time for the pigs. *Splosh!* Charlie the Chimp tipped a bucketful of swill into their trough. The hungry pigs began bolting down the smelly stuff as though it were the most luscious grub in the world. Charlie turned away his head. Horrible beasts! No manners at all! Proper pigs, in fact! Nearby, at the next sty, Jack Marsden, Charlie's young master, was busy showing off his prize-winning porker to Farmer Cox.

2—Charlie took no notice of them. That was a pity—for if only Charlie had taken some notice of Farmer Cox, he would have saved himself an awful lot of trouble later on. But he didn't—not until half an hour later anyway. Charlie's work for the day was done, and the smart chimp was quenching his thirst in the garden. Suddenly he spotted a man prodding a pig into a trailer. Charlie leapt to his feet. Jack's prize porker was being stolen.

3—He must save it. Charlie rushed towards the trailer. But he didn't reach it in time to stop the pig being stolen. Already the trailer was on the move. Charlie grabbed the tail-board. He didn't mean to let the porker out of his sight. Charlie scrambled in beside the big pig.

4—Peter the pig glared at Charlie. But before he could figure out whether the chimp was friend or foe, the trailer stopped at the traffic lights. Working fast, Charlie let down the tail-board, then rode the startled pig out of the trailer. "Stop, thief!" roared Farmer Cox angrily.

5—The pig was his. He had bought it from Jack. But Charlie didn't know that. He thought the man had stolen Peter. Charlie rode through the traffic. But he had no means of steering. That was why Charlie presently found himself charging helter-skelter down a country lane.

6—Up and down like a rubber ball Charlie bounced on galloping Peter's back. Grimly he hung on. The road ended. But the ride didn't! Across a field Peter now charged. Ahead lay a pond. Peter stopped suddenly, right on the muddy edge of the pond. Charlie didn't though!

7—He flew like a bird over Peter's head. *Splosh!* Into all that thick, oozy mud Charlie flopped. Peter gave a grunt of satisfaction. Then joined Charlie in the mud! Lovely! Peter wallowed in the cool, soft, caressing mud. Charlie glared fiercely at Peter through mud-ringed eyes.

8—Then he splashed over to Peter and began pushing and pulling. Peter grunted and didn't budge. He was happy just where he was. Charlie gave up struggling and fetched a rope. The chimp tied it around Peter's middle. Then he heaved. Peter didn't move a single, muddy inch!

9—In fact, Peter was a proper stick-in-the mud! But Charlie wasn't beaten. He would get the better of that big, fat pig! When Charlie is in trouble he takes to the trees. So Charlie climbed up a nearby tree. It was a young tree, and as the chimp climbed higher, it bent under his weight.

10—More and more the tree arched. Presently it was bent almost double, and the top of the tree quivered just a few inches above the wallowing pig. Charlie tied the loose end of the rope to the tree. The other end was still tied round Peter. Charlie gave a little, mischievous snigger.

11—With a final tug at the knot to test it, Charlie leapt off the tree. *Whang!* The tree suddenly catapulted up. And poor, startled Peter took to the air. *Zoom!* Across the sky the flying pig flew, a trail of mud dripping behind. Meanwhile Charlie had got to the pond's edge and was watching.

12—Charlie whooped and cheered with delight as Peter ended his sudden flight. The rope broke, and Peter went hurtling into the pond with a tremendous splash. Peter let out a squeal of horror. Perhaps he hated water. Anyway he made it plain that the quicker he got out, the better he'd like it. Peter paddled towards the bank to get back to where his lovely, soupy mud was. Charlie didn't let him though. He was waiting and grabbed Peter by the ear. Then he got busy washing all the mud off the dirty big pig.

13—Charlie couldn't possibly take the prize porker home in such an awful mess. But he had only a hankie—a very small one at that—and Peter was a very large pig to wash down. The job took ages. And Peter didn't help. He jumped and wriggled.

14—The noise attracted Farmer Cox to the spot. "So this is where you've lured my pig!" he growled fiercely. "And what d'you mean by getting it in a state like that?" Charlie was speechless! After all his efforts, here was the thief come to pinch the pig again! Farmer Cox looked sourly at Charlie. "And you've got yourself in a fine state, too!" he grunted. Charlie certainly had. He was caked over with mud from the top of his head to the tips of his toes!

15—"They'll not let you on a bus like that!" grunted Farmer Cox. "I'll take you home." Before Charlie could move he was forked into the trailer. While Peter went to the farm with a lad, Charlie was driven home by the farmer. "Brought the pig back?" Jack Marsden asked. "Yes!" grinned Farmer Cox. And he opened the trailer. Out trooped Charlie, dirtier than any pig. Poor fellow! He'd got himself in a mess for nothing, prize chump that he was!

A company with good taste has used my handsome face to **PLUG** their product . . . hur! hur! . . . and Robert Harrap Designs has produced a whole range of BEANO and DANDY collectable figurines. It's the first time anyone's seen The Bash Street Kids standing still.

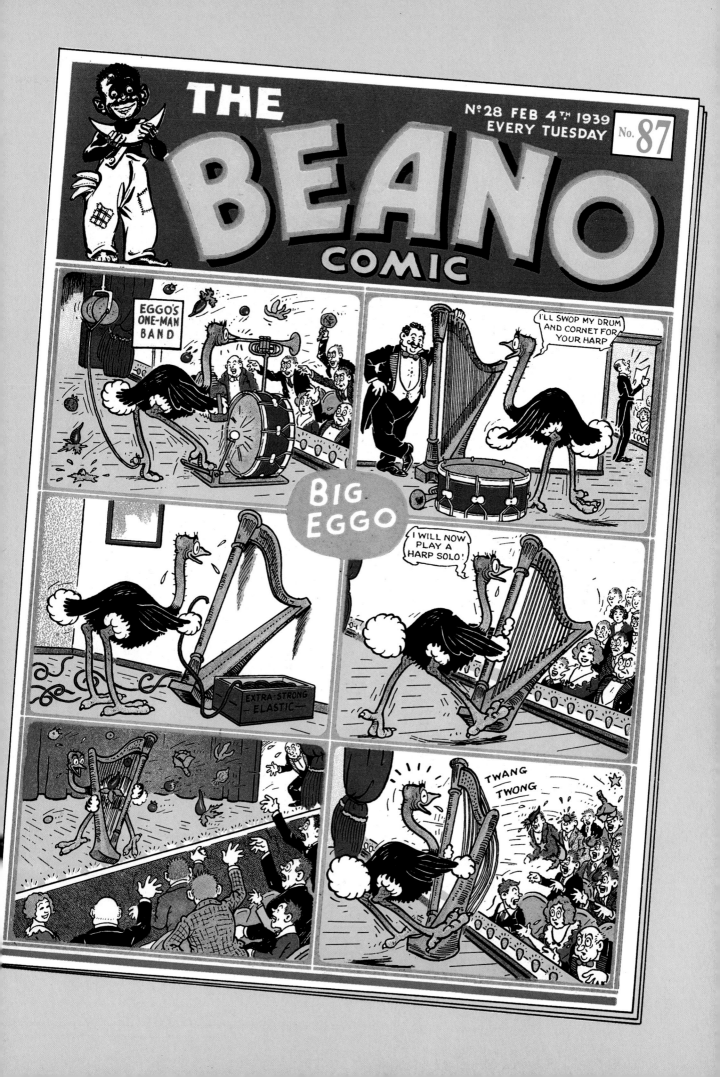

SMIFFY'S 101

You probably already knew that **Korky The Cat** and **Desperate Dan** appeared in the first ever DANDY on December 4, 1937. But did you know that same comic featured long-forgotten stories like **The Tricks Of Tommy**, **Red Hoof** and **Boaster Billy**?

All good comic fans will know that **Lord Snooty** first starred in BEANO'S first issue on July 30, 1938. But not so many will remember **Ping The Elastic Man** or **Big Fat Joe** from issue number one.

A story called **The Smasher** appeared in DANDY, way back in 1938. But that tale didn't feature the walking disaster area popular with today's readers. The original **Smasher** was a robot, while the smash-'em bash-'em schoolboy didn't arrive until 1957.

In 1988 the BBC arts programme Arena devoted almost an hour to DANDY and BEANO. The comics' editors and script writers appeared on screen to talk about their work.

Many comic characters including **Roger The Dodger** and **Minnie The Minx** have appeared on Cadbury's Easter Eggs.

FORE! Well, two actually. That's the number of **Dennis The Menace** golf books available. **Don't Be A Golf Menace** is a booklet of tips, quips, dos and don'ts for young golfers. **The Rules Of Golf According To Dennis The Menace** is a handsome hardback with an amusing, but totally accurate, account of the rules of the game.

DON'T BE A GOLF MENACE

EASY-TO-FOLLOW GUIDELINE FOR GOLFERS

THE RULES OF GOLF

according to DENNIS the MENACE

with the reluctant approval of The Royal and Ancient Golf Club of St. Andrews

FASCINATING FACTS

The BEANO superstars invaded Coronation Street . . . well, almost. December 1994, and an advert for the BEANO Videostars was broadcast during the ad-break in the middle of Britain's favourite soap.

Believe it or not, **Black Bob**, the DANDY Wonderdog, has had eight annuals all to himself while comic-world legend, **Desperate Dan**, has only had four.

Dennis The Menace is no softie but there was a time when people walked all over him — that was when a **Dennis** rug appeared in the shops.

Cuddles And Dimples are now firm favourites in DANDY but the terrible twosome didn't even start out in the same comic. **Cuddles** made his first appearance in the now-defunct NUTTY comic while **Dimples'** debut was in DANDY.

When **Dennis** first appeared in The Beano in 1951, he didn't wear his famous hooped jersey but he DID wear a tie (sounds a bit soft, doesn't it!)

What gets your vote as the strangest story title to appear in DANDY or BEANO? Here are a few to choose from — Bertie Buncle And His Chemical Uncle, Big Chief Itchy Snitch, Digger's Wandering Wardrobe, Our Teacher's A Walrus, The King With The Cauliflower Conk, Sandy's Magic Bagpipes.

Back in the early 1980s, before he'd made his first appearance in the pages of DANDY, **Bananaman** was already a TV star with his own cartoon series.

The first BEANO annual was published in time for Christmas 1939 and cost the equivalent of 13p.

Well, er, um . . . that's 101 facts, I think!

Don't believe it, readers! Smiffy can't count and THAT'S a fact!

THE FRONT PAGE BOY

We all remember the famous names from DANDY'S early years — Desperate Dan, Korky The Cat, Keyhole Kate . . . but what about the boy who appeared on the comic's cover each week from 1937 until 1960. His name won't ring a bell, but Bellboy stood smiling next to the DANDY title welcoming readers to another fun-packed issue. He didn't have a story of his own but often popped up inside the comic — running, cycling, jumping — always smiling.

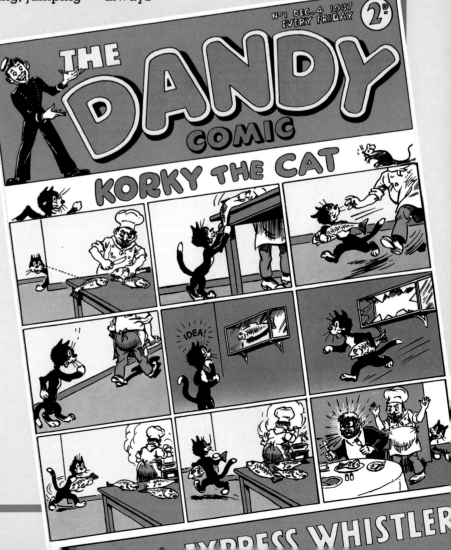